ALL TIME STANDARDS

Music arranged and processed by Barnes Music Engraving Ltd, East Sussex TN22 4HA, England
Cover design by xheight Limited
Published 1996

BEWITCHED

Words by LORENZ HART
Music by RICHARD RODGERS

Registration	
Upper:	Vibraphone
Lower:	Piano / Strings
Pedal:	8' Acoustic Bass
Rhythm	Swing
Tempo	♩ = 74

Freely
rhythm off

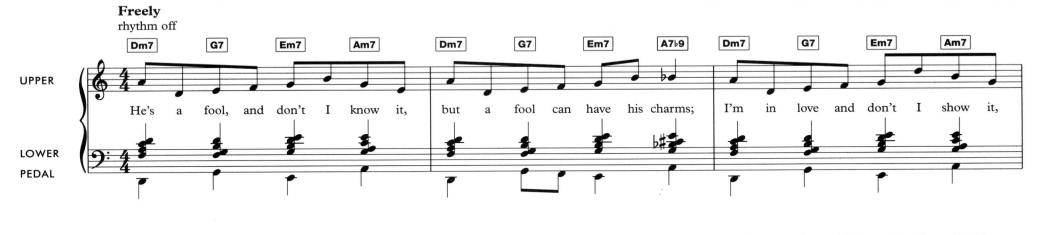

UPPER / LOWER / PEDAL

He's a fool, and don't I know it, but a fool can have his charms; I'm in love and don't I show it,

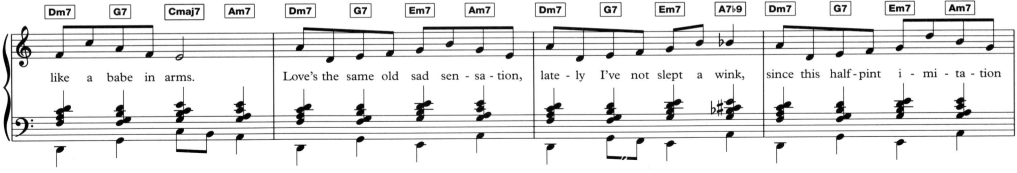

like a babe in arms. Love's the same old sad sen - sa - tion, late - ly I've not slept a wink, since this half - pint i - mi - ta - tion

a tempo
rhythm start

(Drum fill)   **rit.**

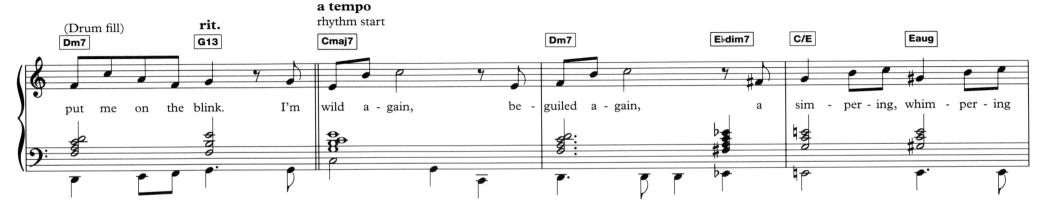

put me on the blink. I'm wild a - gain, be - guiled a - gain, a sim - per - ing, whim - per - ing

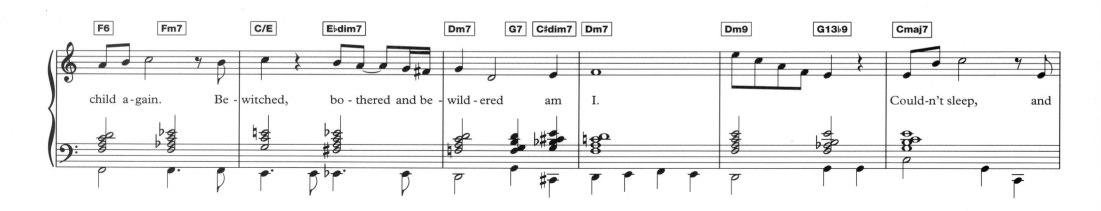

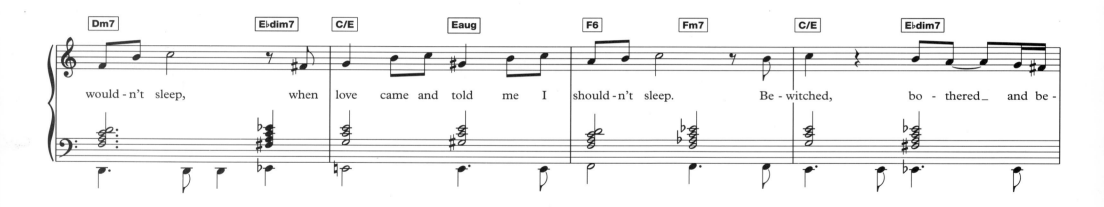

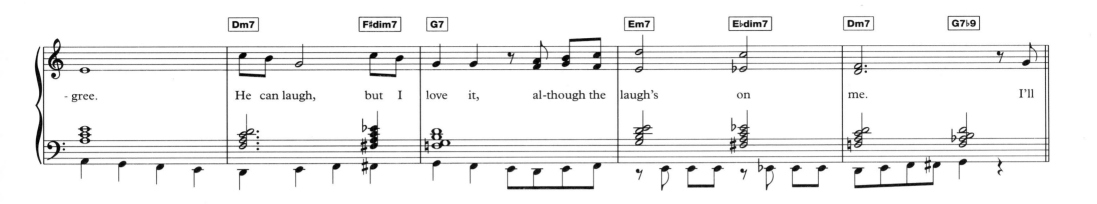

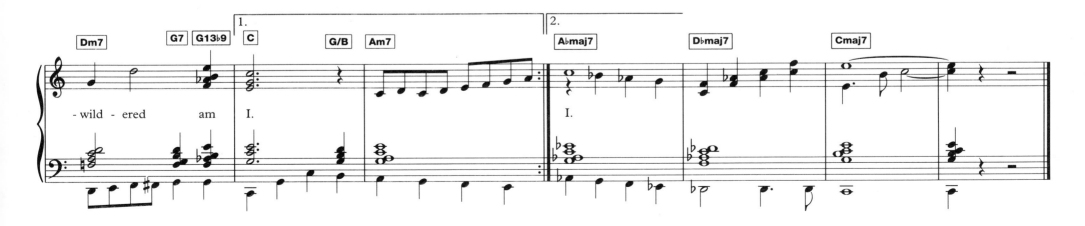

CRAZY RHYTHM

Words by IRVING CAESAR
Music by JOSEPH MEYER and ROGER WOLFE KAHN

Registration
Upper: Pop Organ
Lower: Piano / Brass
Pedal: 8' Acoustic Bass
Rhythm   Bright Swing
Tempo   ♩ = 158

CHEEK TO CHEEK

Words and Music by IRVING BERLIN

Registration
Upper: Piano / Vibes / Guitar
Lower: Piano / Strings
Pedal: 8' Acoustic Bass
Rhythm Swing or Bounce
Tempo ♩ = 170

9

I REMEMBER YOU

Words by JOHNNY MERCER
Music by VICTOR SCHERTZINGER

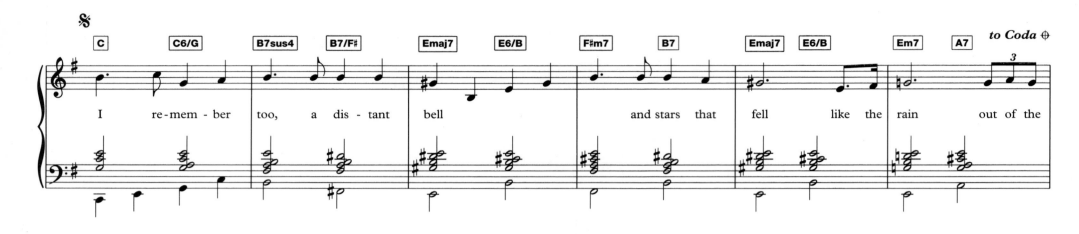

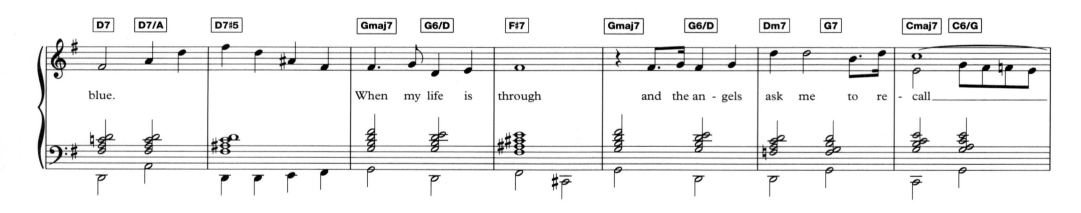

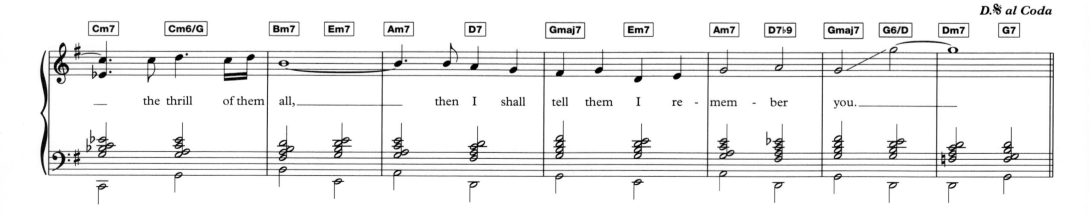

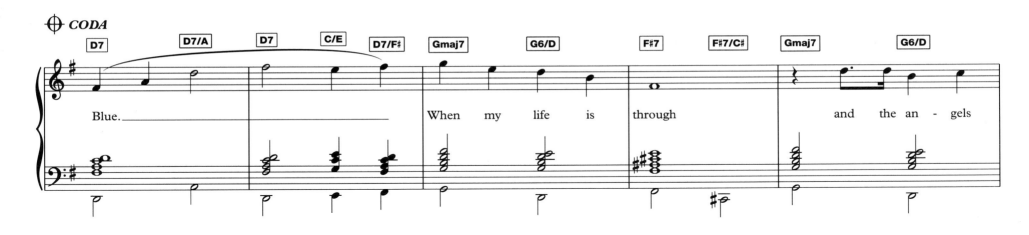

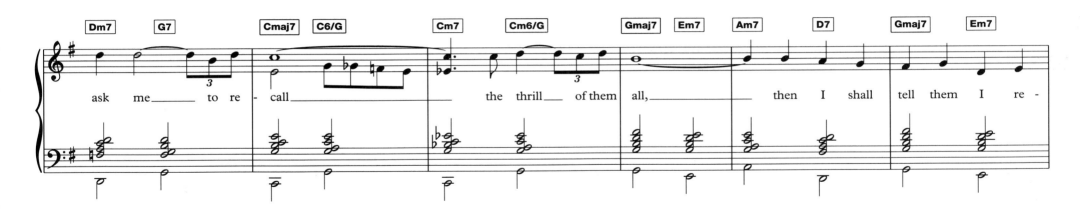

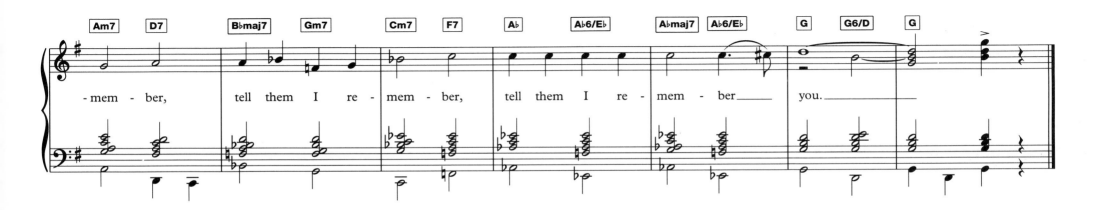

IT'S MAGIC

Words by SAMMY CAHN
Music by JULE STYNE

Registration
Upper: Pop Organ (alternate fast and slow tremulant)
Lower: Strings / Organ
Pedal: 8' Bass Guitar
Rhythm Bossa Nova
Tempo ♩ = 94

14

IT'S ONLY A PAPER MOON

Words by BILLY ROSE and E Y HARBURG
Music by HAROLD ARLEN

Registration
Upper: 8' Piano
Lower: Strings / Electric Piano
Pedal: 8' Acoustic Bass
Rhythm Big Band Swing
Tempo ♩ = 136

MONA LISA

Words and Music by JAY LIVINGSTON and RAY EVANS

Registration
Upper: ① Trombone Lead, ② Pop Organ
Lower: Piano / Strings
Pedal: 8' Acoustic Bass
Rhythm: Swing
Tempo: ♩ = 80

MOON RIVER

Words by JOHNNY MERCER
Music by HENRY MANCINI

Registration
Upper: Orch. Strings / Solo Violin
Lower: Strings / Piano
Pedal: 8' Acoustic Bass
Rhythm   Waltz
Tempo   ♩ = 84

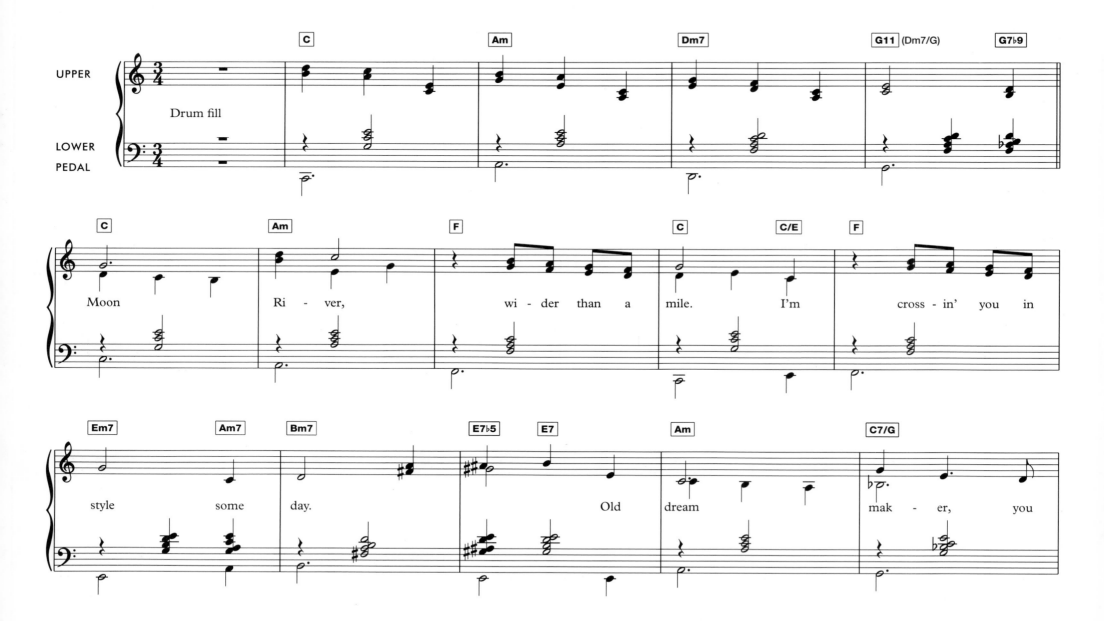

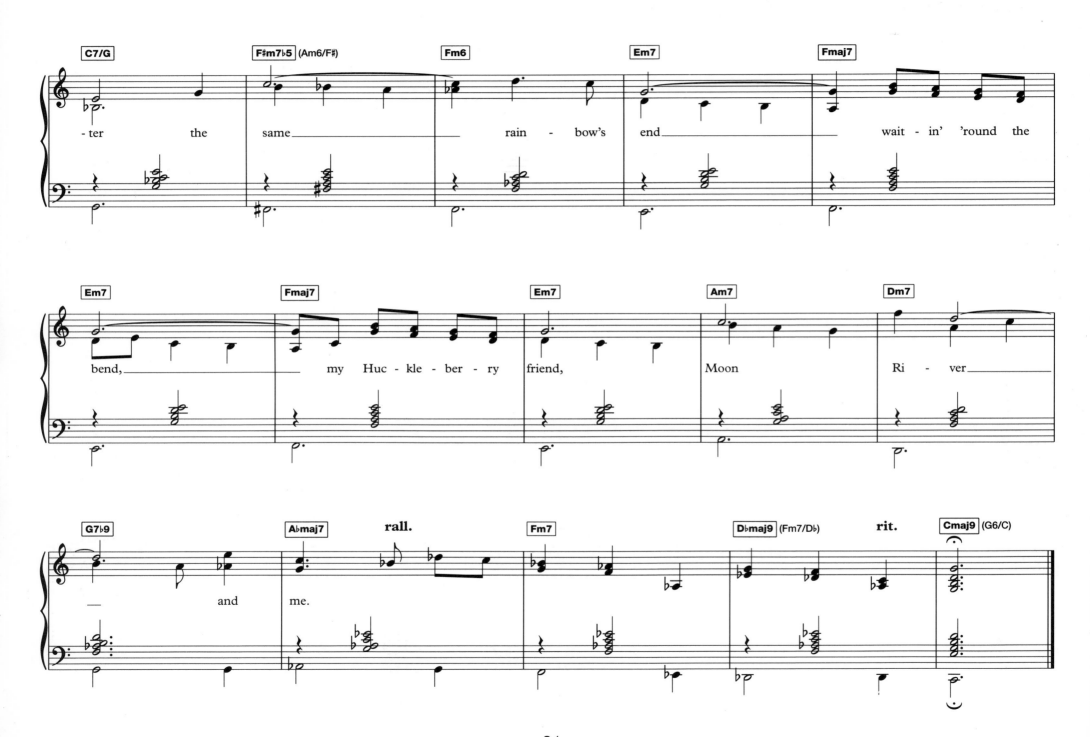

THE NEARNESS OF YOU

Words by NED WASHINGTON
Music by HOAGY CARMICHAEL

Registration
Upper: Strings / Solo Flute or Strings / Oboe
Lower: Strings / Electric Piano
Pedal: 8' Acoustic Bass
Rhythm   Bossa Nova or Beguine
Tempo   ♩ = 85

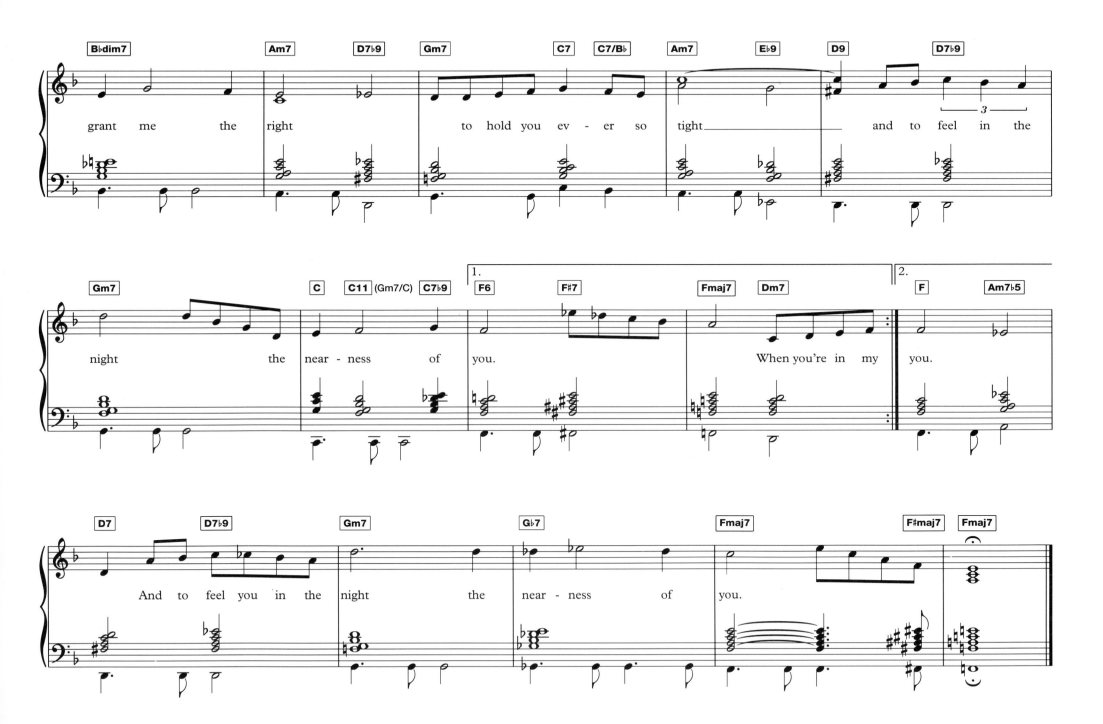

SECRET LOVE

Words by PAUL FRANCIS WEBSTER
Music by SAMMY FAIN

Registration
Upper: Strings / Piano
Lower: Strings / Pop Organ
Pedal: 8' Acoustic Bass
Rhythm   Rhumba
Tempo   ♩ = 104

29

SECRET LOVE

30

SEPTEMBER SONG

Words by MAXWELL ANDERSON
Music by KURT WEILL

Registration
Upper: Vibraphone
Lower: Strings / Pop Organ
Pedal: 8' Acoustic Bass
Rhythm   Swing
Tempo   ♩ = 112

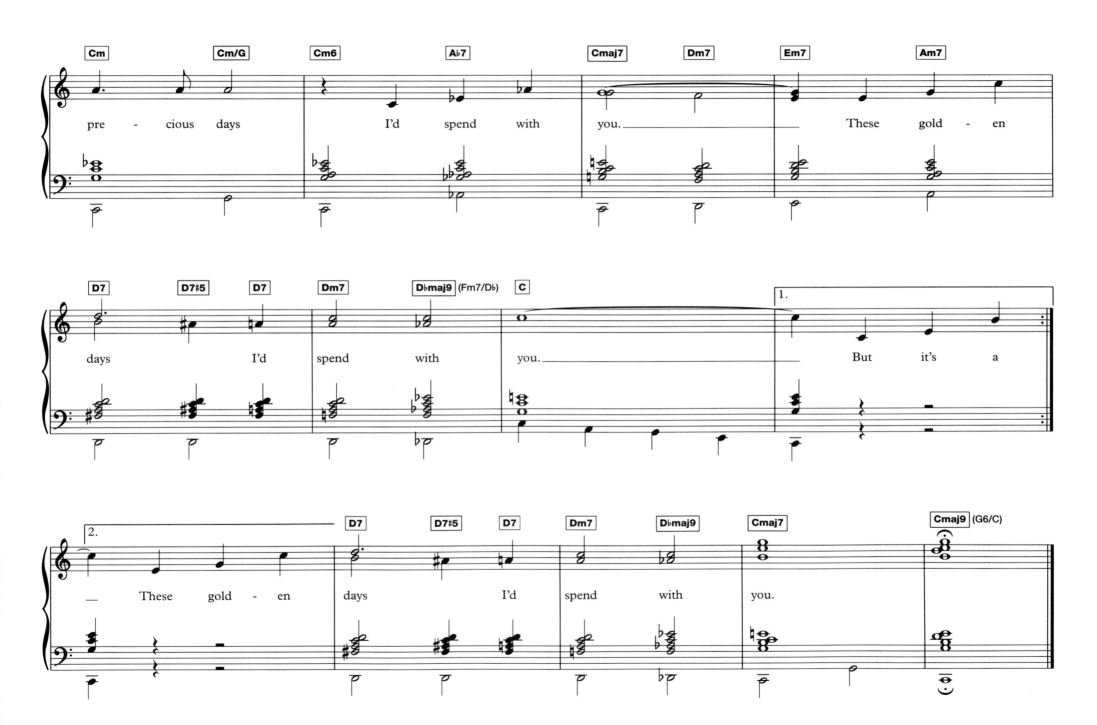

SOMEONE TO WATCH OVER ME

Music and Lyrics by GEORGE GERSHWIN and IRA GERSHWIN

Registration
Upper: Pop Organ
Lower: Organ / Strings
Pedal: 8' Electric Bass
Rhythm Beguine
Tempo ♩ = 90

WHEN I FALL IN LOVE

Words by EDWARD HEYMAN
Music by VICTOR YOUNG

Registration
Upper: Piano / Vibes / Jazz Guitar
Lower: Strings / Piano
Pedal: 8' Acoustic Bass
Rhythm Swing
Tempo ♩ = 94

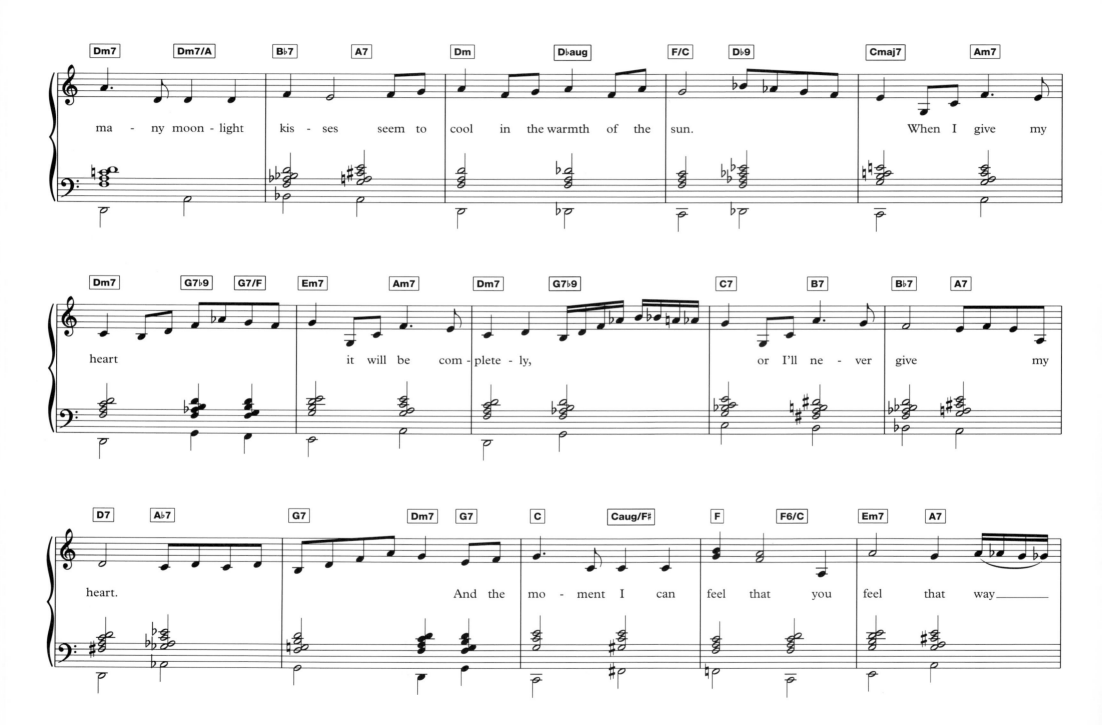

THAT OLD BLACK MAGIC

Words by JOHNNY MERCER
Music by HAROLD ARLEN

Registration
Upper: Pop Organ
Lower: Brass / Strings
Pedal: 8' Electric Bass
Rhythm   Samba
Tempo   ♩ = 106

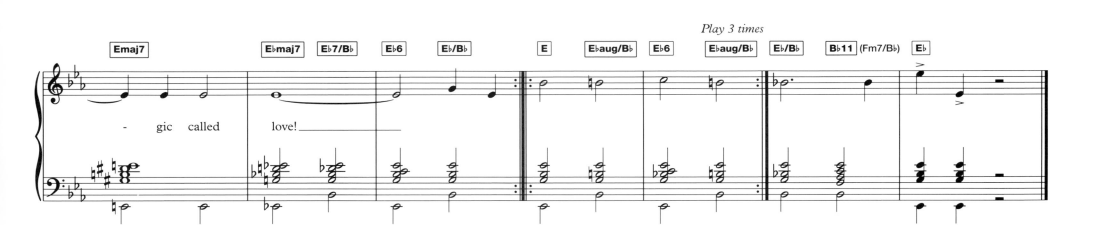

Play 3 times

YOU MAKE ME FEEL SO YOUNG

Words by MACK GORDON
Music by JOSEF JOE MYROW

Registration
Upper: Jazz Organ
Lower: Organ / Strings
Pedal: 8' Acoustic Bass
Rhythm   Swing
Tempo   ♩ = 114

Printed in England
Panda Press · Haverhill · Suffolk · 2/96

also available in this series:

All Time Standards

Bewitched	Moon River
Cheek To Cheek	The Nearness Of You
Crazy Rhythm	Secret Love
I Remember You	September Song
It's Magic	Someone To Watch Over Me
It's Only A Paper Moon	That Old Black Magic
Mona Lisa	When I Fall In Love
You Make Me Feel So Young	

Order Ref: 3509A

Showtunes

Almost Like Being In Love	Getting To Know You
Anything Goes	Hello Dolly!
Bali Ha'i	I've Grown Accustomed To Her Face
Cabaret	My Favorite Things
The Colors Of My Life	Oh, What A Beautiful Mornin'
Consider Yourself	Smoke Gets In Your Eyes
A Foggy Day	They Can't Take That Away From Me
You'll Never Walk Alone	

Order Ref: 3512A

Film Hits

Alfie	I Have Nothing
Arthur's Theme (Best That You Can Do)	(I've Had) The Time Of My Life
Big Spender	La Bamba
Bright Eyes	Raindrops Keep Fallin' On My Head
Endless Love	The Sound Of Music
Evergreen	Star Wars (Main Theme)
For Your Eyes Only	Summer Holiday
Tara's Theme	

Order Ref: 3510A

Easy Listening

Always On My Mind	Laughter In The Rain
Chanson D'Amour	Moonlighting
Earth Angel	Now And Forever
Everybody's Talkin'	The Rose
Goodbye Girl	Trains And Boats And Planes
If I Were A Carpenter	We Don't Cry Out Loud
It's All In The Game	Why Do Fools Fall In Love?
You Make Me Feel Brand New	

Order Ref: 3513A

Love Songs

I Can't Give You Anything But Love	Tenderly
I Just Called To Say I Love You	Three Times A Lady
I'll Be There	Too Marvellous For Words
Killing Me Softly With His Song	Up Where We Belong
Let's Do It (Let's Fall In Love)	The Way You Look Tonight
Love Is A Many-Splendoured Thing	Where Do I Begin? (Love Story)
Love Is Here To Stay	With You I'm Born Again
My Foolish Heart	You Light Up My Life
You'll Never Know	

Order Ref: 3511A

Solid Gold Hits

Don't Let The Sun Go Down On Me	Oh, Pretty Woman
Eternal Flame	The Power Of Love
A Horse With No Name	Save The Best For Last
Hotel California	Solitaire
I Got You Babe	Stand By Me
Nights In White Satin	What A Wonderful World
A Whiter Shade Of Pale	

Order Ref: 3514A